Second Edition Revised

ECONOMICS

New Ways of Thinking

Finding Economics

Daniel R. Arnold
Roger A. Arnold

St. Paul, Minnesota

Publisher: Alex Vargas
Managing Editor: Brenda Owens
Production Manager: Bob Dreas
Cover Designer: Leslie Anderson
Design and Production Specialist: Tammy Norstrem

ISBN 978-1-53383-492-8

875 Montreal Way
St. Paul, MN 55102
Email: educate@emcp.com
Website: www.emcschool.com

Printed in the United States of America

27 26 25 24 23 22 21 20 19 18 1 2 3 4 5 6 7 8 9 10

CONTENTS

PREFACE

When we watch a movie, we watch as a story unfolds in front of us. If it is a good movie with a good story, we are pulled into it. We watch others, and, at the same time, live their experiences. If we did not have the ability to empathize—to feel what others are feeling—movies would not be as enjoyable.

If you break a movie into small parts, you have scenes. A movie director sees a movie as a succession of scenes. For example, in Scene 1, Emily runs for the subway; in Scene 14, Quincy has dinner with a fri
who has just returned from Bangkok; in Scene 28, Emily and Quincy argue over
editing room, the different scenes are cut and pasted together to tell a story.

Life is full of stories, but even more, life is full of scenes. And sometimes
the way scenes in a movie do. Life's scenes aren't always a part of a bigg
and go to school, you have lunch with friends, you watch some
chat online for awhile, and you go to bed. D
life.

In this book you will find scenes from t
won't always know what came before or w
hotel restaurant and meets her mother fr
what happened in Scene 34 or what will
this is what often happens in life.

Often in life there are also things goi We believe
that many of life's scenes are about mor bition,
greed, friendship, longing, and so on.

And here's the kicker: sometimes t

That's right. Sometimes below the That doesn't mean it
is easy to see the economics below th ave to dig for it. But once you
find it, you may say, "Well, sure; it w why I couldn't see it at first."

In this book you will find scenes e lives of various people—a woman who works at the Metropolitan Museum of Art in New Yo , a best-selling horror novelist, a high school senior who is
preparing for college, a family eat ner, four friends on their first trip to Europe, and more.

Read the scenes from the lives e people. Try to get into their worlds. And while you're there, look
for the economics.

Daniel R. Arnold and Roger A. Arnold

Name: ______________________________ Date: ______________

CHAPTER 1

Before you read the following scene, review Chapter 1 in the *Student Text,* focusing on the major concepts covered there. You may want to skim the chapter or read the Chapter Summary on page 30.

Now, with the economics concepts of Chapter 1 fresh in your mind, read "Jessica Pauline Jones," searching, like an economics detective, for the economics below the surface. The story contains a number of economics ideas, but they are hidden. It is your job to find them.

As you read, circle and underline words and phrases that you think are clues or connections to the economics embedded in the scene. Make notes in the margin. At the end of the scene, on the lines provided, write two or three sentences describing each of the three most interesting economics ideas that you found in the scene.

Jessica Pauline Jones

Notes

Jessica Pauline Jones, 28 years old, works at 1000 Fifth Avenue in New York City. That is the home of the world famous Metropolitan Museum of Art. In front of the grand museum are Fifth Avenue and the whole Upper East Side of New York; behind the museum are the 843 acres that comprise Central Park. For an art major from Wellesley College who also earned a Master of Fine Arts from Cornell, it was one of the greatest places in the world to work.

Starbucks coffee in hand, Jessica walked up the steps of the subway exit at 86th Street. As she reached ground level, she saw, as she did every morning at this time, the street dancers in front of the museum. As hip-hop music pumped out of a large portable CD player, five young men, probably in their late teens and early 20s, danced for the crowd that waited for the museum to open. Their objective was to amaze and entertain the crowd with their dance moves, and they were quite successful in this goal. One dancer placed a black baseball cap, upside down, out in front of the group, where the crowd showed its appreciation with some change and a few dollars.

Yellow taxis and city buses with screeching brakes flowed through the traffic on Fifth Avenue in front of the museum. People walked quickly, eyes ahead, many of them conducting early morning business on their cell phones, and a nanny with a stroller crossed the street to enter the park.

At the top of the many steps leading to the museum's front entrance, Jessica showed a badge and the security guard let her in. Her low-heeled shoes clicked as she walked across the floor to the elevator. She went up to the third floor, walked down the hall, and into her office. The sign on her door read: Jessica Jones, Special Exhibitions. She had been preparing for the upcoming Matisse Exhibition, which was to begin in only eight days.

Merely four minutes after Jessica sat down at her desk, her phone rang, and caller ID showed her that it was Darren calling. She had met him only two weeks ago, but already she was falling for him. He was attractive and bright and had a good sense of humor. These are things that one doesn't usually find in a quant. Of course, she didn't know what a quant was when he first told her he was one.

"What do you do?" she had asked, not long after he first came up to talk with her.

"I'm a quant," he said that day. He thought that she might not know what that was (most people didn't), so he quickly followed with the words, "That's a mathematician of sorts; one who deals mostly with financial instruments—you know, stocks, bonds, futures, options, that kind of thing."

"Do you sell stocks and bonds, too?" Jessica questioned.

Darren laughed and said, "No, there's no way my boss would let me come near selling anything. Nerds aren't supposed to be able to sell anything, you know."

"So, you're a nerd?" Jessica asked.

"That's what the people I work with—you know, the other people in the firm—usually think of quants. They see quants as math nerds, capable of mathematical feats, but incapable of doing things like having a simple conversation with a person."

"You seem to be doing pretty well right now," Jessica had said as she smiled at him.

In her office, she picked up the phone and said hello in a not-quite-official voice.

"Did you just get in?" Darren asked.

"Just a few minutes ago," she said. "How are you?"

"I'm doing fine," he said. "I enjoyed having dinner at that Thai restaurant last night," he added.

"I did too," Jessica said. "It was fun."

"What about lunch today? Do you have time?" he asked.

"Are you sure you have the time?" she countered.

"Yeah, I do," he said. Usually he just ate a sandwich at his desk, but today he wanted to get out; he wanted to see Jessica.

"Well, then, sure, I can do it," she said.

"No problem getting away from Matisse?" he asked.

"Matisse is doing all right," she said. "I can take a little time away from him."

"I'll meet you out front at, say, one, if that's OK," he said.

"That'll be great," she said. She then looked up and saw Kareem, her colleague, standing at her door. Good timing, she thought; the conversation was over anyway. "See you then," she said to Darren, and then she hung up the phone.

Find the Economics

Name the three most interesting economics ideas that you found "hidden" in this scene, and explain the clues that led you to discover them.

1. ______________________________

____

____

2. ______________________________

____

____

3. ______________________________

____

____

Name: ______________________________ Date: ______________

CHAPTER 2

Before you read the following scene, review Chapter 2 in the *Student Text*, focusing on the major concepts covered there. You may want to skim the chapter or read the Chapter Summary on page 58.

Now, with the economics concepts of Chapter 2 fresh in your mind, read "On a Kansas Road Late at Night," searching, lik[illegible] economics detective, for the economics below the surface. The story contain[illegible] of economics ideas, but they are hidden. It is your job to find them.

As you read, circle and underli[illegible]d phrases that you think are clues or connections to the economics embe[illegible] scene. Make notes in the margin. At the end of the scene, on the lines provi[illegible]vo or three sentences describing each of the three most interesting economi[illegible] you found in the scene.

On a Kansas Road Late a[illegible]

Notes

You can get some flat stret[illegible] the Midwest. One night two years ago I was [illegible]ntucky to Colorado. At the time, I was crossing Kansa[illegible] 11:30 p.m. I sort of like driving at that time of night. Th[illegible]any cars out on the roads, and everything seems [illegible] peaceful. I don't know, but it's always felt to me like [illegible]till—and that's not a feeling I get during the dayti[illegible] be moving fast then.

Anyway, it was just me [illegible]dio on. I like talk radio, and there was this host-[illegible]e now—on the radio talking to people who w[illegible]r away as Seattle.

You can hear some [illegible]g in to talk radio shows at 11:30 at night. Som[illegible]n want to talk about UFOs, and this conspiracy and that [illegible] and why tomorrow the world is going to end, and all that kind of stuff. Some of it I find entertaining, although I don't believe everything that is said. I just like listening to different types of people talk about whatever is on their minds at the time.

That night while I drove through Kansas, one caller started talking about all the jobs that were leaving the United States and going overseas. He said it was going to be the ruin of the country. "Before long," he said, "the only thing we'll be doing in the United States is flipping burgers, and that's because there is no drive-up window that runs through India or China."

The talk show host told him that things weren't that bad, and then he said something about the world getting smaller, and the United States entering a global economy, and then the caller said again that America was headed for hard times, and then we were on to a new caller. I can't remember what the new caller wanted to talk about.

It was that night that I started thinking. If we were moving into a global economy, wouldn't that potentially mean more customers for me—assuming I started a business, that is. I'd been thinking about starting my own business for about three years now, but I hadn't gotten around to it. If the truth be known, I was sort of afraid of going at it alone. Where do you start? How do you get a loan? Where do you buy your supplies? How do you get the word out that you're in business and ready to sell to the people you hope are equally ready to buy? I have to tell you, I respect those people who start their own businesses. I always thought they had to be smart. But recently I've changed my mind about that. I know a lot of smart people, people who have done well in school and at college, who couldn't figure out how to start their own businesses. I think it takes a kind of courage to strike out on your own—that's what I think it takes to start your own business too.

Something about listening to that call on that talk radio show that night gave me courage. That night, on the roads of Kansas, dark as could be, with only my headlights to lead the way, something in my head clicked. I saw myself selling to the whole world.

When I got back to Kentucky three weeks later, I started to work. I wanted to make toys, but not just any toys. I wanted to make toys that were both inexpensive and different. Ever since I had been young, I had always thought about certain toys that I would have liked to have, but that didn't exist. For example, I always thought it would be nice to have a radio that not only played music but blew bubbles too. Every time you changed either the station or the volume, bubbles would come out of the radio. I also thought about a ball with the hands of a clock on it. Every time you bounced the ball, the hands of the clock would change to a new time. I thought that would be a good toy to teach young children how to tell time. Bounce the ball, tell the time; bounce the ball, tell the time.

I started searching for someone to design the toys and eventually I found just the right person. I went to a bank and got a loan and then I set out to find a company to manufacture the toys. I started with a company in the United States, but eventually I found out how much cheaper it would be to get the toys manufactured in Hong Kong. Now I go to Hong Kong for long periods at a time.

Two years after starting my business, my toys are being sold in 17 countries around the world. My biggest market is the United States. About half of all the toys I make are sold in the United States. Every now and then I go into stores to see what is selling and what isn't, and to get ideas for new toys. I sometimes see a small child, about four or five years old, looking up at one of the toys I made and telling her mother she wants the toy. That makes me feel good.

By the way, if you were wondering about the radio that blew bubbles and the ball-clock, the radio that blew bubbles was a big flop. The ball-clock, believe it or not, was a big hit. I would have thought it would be the other way around.

Find the Economics

Name the three most interesting economics ideas that you found "hidden" in this scene, and explain the clues that led you to discover them.

1. ____

____

____

2. ____

____

____

3. ____

____

____

Name: ______________________ Date: ____________

CHAPTER 3

Before you read the following scene, review Chapter 3 in the *Student Text,* focusing on the major concepts covered there. You may want to skim the chapter or read the Chapter Summary on page 90.

Now, with the economics concepts of Chapter 3 fresh in your mind, read "Morning on the Freeway," searching, like an economics detective, for the economics below the surface. The story contains a number of economics ideas, but they are hidden. It is your job to find them.

As you read, circle and underline words and phrases that you think are clues or connections to the economics embedded in the scene. Make notes in the margin. At the end of the scene, on the lines provided, write two or three sentences describing each of the three most interesting economics ideas that you found in the scene.

Morning on the Freeway

Notes

In southern California, around eight o'clock on weekday mornings, there is a lot of life on the freeways.

Vashti Patel, 38, sits in her five-year-old car, listens to the radio, and drives at about 10 miles an hour. Things are moving slower today than usual; there is an accident up ahead. But even without the accident, traffic generally moves fairly slowly.

Vashti is listening to KITV, her favorite music station. Lately, she has been thinking of signing up with one of the satellite stations. "Too many commercials," she mumbles under her breath. During the morning commute, the commercials are frequent and long. She pushes the station buttons on her radio and finds only one station that isn't currently playing a commercial.

To Vashti's right, Melanie Becker sits in a brand new BMW 5 Series sedan. She bought the car last week because, as she put it, "I work so hard, I deserve it." She works as an attorney at a local law firm. Melanie hopes to make partner in a few years, so she works nearly 75 hours a week. When she was 22 and thinking about going to law school, she never thought she'd end up working as much as she has. She tells her friends that she doesn't mind the work, but often late at night, after a long day, she does mind it. Every now and then she even wonders if she went into the right profession.

In the far left lane, a police car, siren roaring, is trying to make its way through to the accident up ahead.

On Vashti's left, loud music blares from a yellow Mustang driven by a young man, probably around 19 years old. "Who does this guy think he is?" Vashti wonders. "Doesn't he realize that he's bothering everyone around him? How does he expect us to listen to what we want to listen to with his music blasting away?"

Three cars ahead of Vashti, in the lane to her right, Carlos Ortiz is on his hands-free cell phone talking to Mike Kubin, who is in Boulder, Colorado. Carlos and Mike work for the same company, which manufactures and sells running shoes. Carlos is one of five regional managers for the company and Mike is a new sales representative, only one month on the job.

"What don't they like about the shoe?" Carlos asks.

"They say that it looks too much like an 'old shoe' to them. At least, that's what Max said."

"Tell them the shoes are selling well just about everywhere. That should prove that it's not being considered an old shoe by others."

"I told him that. I even showed him the list of places that are currently carrying the shoe. He still doesn't want it."

"Maybe we can go down a bit on our price. I'm going to check with Frank in the office; I'll get back to you later."

"OK. Talk to you later, then. Bye."

"Bye."

Vashti is past the accident now and traffic is moving a little faster. LaToya Chambers, in a car that just ahead of Vashti on her left, is listening to *Marketplace* from American Public Media. The story is about Janet Yellen, the chair of the Board of Governors of the Federal Reserve System.

Vashti takes the Del Mar Heights Road exit and drives two more miles to her office. She gets out of her car, walks into the building, and takes the elevator up to the fifth floor. When the elevator door opens, she steps out and walks the 25 steps—she counts them each day—to her office. She opens the door, says good morning to whomever she sees, and then sits down at her computer. For Vashti, the workday has officially begun.

Find the Economics

Name the three most interesting economics ideas that you found "hidden" in this scene, and explain the clues that led you to discover them.

1. ______________________________

____

____

2. ______________________________

____

____

3. ______________________________

____

____

Name: ______________________________ Date: ______________

CHAPTER 4

Before you read the following scene, review Chapter 4 in the *Student Text*, focusing on the major concepts that are covered there. You may want to skim the chapter or read the Chapter Summary on page 120.

Now, with the economics concepts of Chapter 4 fresh in your mind, read "Moving to Atlanta," searching, like an economics detective, for the economics below the surface of the story. The story contains a number of economics ideas, but they are hidden. It is your job to find them.

As you read, circle and underline words and phrases that you think are clues or connections to the economics embedded in the scene. Make notes in the margin. At the end of the scene, on the lines provided, write two or three sentences describing each of the three most interesting economics ideas that you found in the scene.

Moving to Atlanta

Notes

Dana moved into the blue house on the corner of Peachtree Lane in August. Her father had lost his job in Seattle six months earlier, and he had found a new one in Atlanta. When he told Dana that they had to move, she was understandably upset. What high school student wants to pick up and travel across the country in her junior year?

"Can't I just stay here for a year?" she asked her parents. "I'm sure Robin's mom will let me live with them," she added. Robin had been Dana's best friend since the third grade.

"I know it's hard on you," Dana's mother said. "But you'll adjust. It may be a little hard in the beginning, but things will get better with time. After all, don't you want to stay with the family?"

Well, of course I want to stay with the family, Dana thought; it's just that the family doesn't seem to want to stay where I want to stay. Whoever heard of dragging your daughter out of her high school in her junior year? Didn't her parents know that abrupt and drastic changes like this could deeply and adversely affect someone? I can see myself years from now, Dana thought, sitting in some psychiatrist's office trying to figure out why I turned out to have so many problems. "Well, doctor," I'll say, "I think it all started when my parents dragged me across the country at the tender age of seventeen..."

Nevertheless, Dana had said goodbye to her friends, gotten into the black Honda Pilot with her mother, father, and younger brother, Paul (who didn't want to move either), and started the journey from Seattle to Atlanta, a total of almost 2,700 miles. The house had been packed up three days before. All the family's furniture, clothes, computers, dishes, pots and pans, and just about everything else was on a huge truck being driven by two strong strangers from the moving company.

Dana knew Seattle; it had been her home for her entire life. She knew next to nothing about Atlanta, and she was a little nervous about the move. After her parents had returned from a visit to find a house there, she asked her mother what the city was really like. What Dana meant was, What will my new life there be like? Will the kids my age accept me? Will I get along with them, and will we have things in common? But Dana hadn't asked these questions, mainly because she wasn't sure why she was feeling uneasy about going to this new place.

But she discovered the reason on her very first day of school in Atlanta. That day her unsettled feeling skyrocketed. "At 8:35 a.m., Dana's slight unease has turned to panic," said the on-the-scene reporter in her head. "That queasy feeling in her stomach has just reached a 9 on the Richter scale, and if she opens her mouth to talk, she is not sure that the words will come out correctly, in the right order."

She walked to the school administration office and told the woman at the counter that her name was Dana Petty and that she was supposed to start school today.

"Oh, yes," the school assistant said. "You're from Seattle, aren't you?"

"Yes, I am," Dana said.

"Well, welcome," the school assistant added. "We're always happy to have one more good student at our school."

Dana smiled and wondered how the school assistant knew she was a "good student." Maybe she doesn't know, Dana thought; maybe she just says that because it is a positive thing to say. Or maybe she says it because she thinks I'm a bad student and she wants me to try to be a good student. Then Dana realized she was doing it: she was overanalyzing things because she was nervous. She had always done that.

Later that day in her biology lab she made her first friend. His name was Andrew. The only empty seat in the lab was the seat next to Andrew, so that is where the biology teacher had asked Dana to sit.

Andrew said a quick "hi" to Dana when she sat down next to him. Dana smiled and said "hi" back. Then Dana looked at the teacher. She didn't want to get reprimanded for talking in class her first day.

As soon as class was over, Andrew turned to Dana.

"My name is Andrew," he said.

"I'm Dana," Dana said.

"Where are you from?" Andrew asked.

"Seattle," Dana said. Then she added, "A long way from here, I'm afraid to say."

Both Dana and Andrew were beginning to collect their books and notebooks.

"We have lunch right now," Andrew said, "would you like me to show you around the school? Maybe we can get lunch together."

Dana smiled with relief. She didn't want to eat lunch alone. That would just be too hard.

"Sure, that would be great," Dana said. She followed Andrew out of the biology lab to the lunchroom. They sat and talked and ate.

Afterward, Andrew, true to his promise, showed Dana around the school. She was amazed at how many people the football stands could hold. "Football is big around here," Andrew said.

"I can see that," Dana said.

It didn't take long for Andrew to ask Dana if she wanted to go to the football game on Friday night. She said that she would like that.

Friday night, during the game and afterward, everything went smoothly. Dana liked Andrew, and the two talked about going out again soon. So Dana was ready when the phone rang the next afternoon.

"Hi," Andrew said. "Would you like to go to a movie tonight?"

"Oh, I can't," said Dana. "My parents are going to meet some people in my dad's new workplace, and I have to watch my brother."

"OK," said Andrew. There was an uncomfortable pause. Then, "Well, I guess I'll see you in school next week—"

"We could go to the movie tomorrow," Dana interrupted.

Why did I say that? she asked herself as she tried to focus on Andrew's response. It makes me sound desperate, and I don't want to sound desperate—but really, I am! After all, Andrew is the only person I know in all of Atlanta.

Somehow, through all this inner dialogue, Dana heard Andrew say that tomorrow wouldn't work for him, and she managed to tell him that was fine and to hang up with some dignity.

Then she felt sad and lonely. What if that was it, and Andrew didn't want to see her again? Who would she eat lunch with?

If that had been a call from a guy in one of my classes back in Seattle, I wouldn't have felt this way, she thought. I'm sure I would have just assumed that I would see him on Monday and we would find another time to go out. Or at least I wouldn't have felt sad and lonely about the idea that we might not get together again. Why do I feel so differently here in Atlanta?

As time passed, Dana made more friends in Atlanta. It has now been five months since Dana moved to town. She still talks to her friends back in Seattle, but less and less frequently. Two of her best friends are Soo Jin and Liz, classmates at her not-so-new school.

Dana doesn't date Andrew anymore, although she did go out with him several times after the football game. Dana noticed that the more friends she got, the more Andrew wanted to go out with her. It was as if he had to know that Dana had options before he would pursue a relationship with her. Eventually, though, they both realized that they didn't have much in common, and they began to see other people.

"I have a hard time understanding guys sometimes," she often says to Soo Jin and Liz. Soo Jin and Liz agree that it's not always easy.

Find the Economics

Name the three most interesting economics ideas that you found "hidden" in this scene, and explain the clues that led you to discover them.

1. ______________________________

____

____

2. ______________________________

____

____

3. ______________________________

____

____

Name: ______________________________ Date: ______________

CHAPTER 5

Before you read the following scene, review Chapter 5 in the *Student Text*, focusing on the major concepts covered there. You may want to skim the chapter or read the Chapter Summary on page 140.

Now, with the economics concepts of Chapter 5 fresh in your mind, read "It's Only Rock 'n' Roll, But I Like It," searching, like an economics detective, for the economics below the surface. The story contains a number of economics ideas, but they are hidden. It is your job to find them.

As you read, circle and underline words and phrases that you think are clues or connections to the economics embedded in the scene. Make notes in the margin. At the end of the scene, on the lines provided, write two or three sentences describing each of the three most interesting economics ideas that you found in the scene.

It's Only Rock 'n' Roll, But I Like It

Notes

It was 5:30 p.m. on a Friday evening when Anne Marie, 17 years old, and her brother Edwardo, 15 years old, got into Anne Marie's car and left their house. The concert was scheduled to start at 7:30 that night. It would take about 45 minutes to drive to the sports arena, where the two bands were scheduled to play—assuming traffic was light, which it usually wasn't on a Friday.

"I hope we don't hit too much traffic," Anne Marie said.

Edwardo had his earbuds in his ears, listening to his iPod. He was listening to a song he expected to hear later that night from the rock group he and Anne Marie were going to see.

Anne Marie looked over at Edwardo and repeated louder, "I hope we don't hit too much traffic."

Edwardo looked up. "What?" he said. He took the left earbud out of his ear.

Anne Marie said the words for the third time. "I said, I hope we don't hit too much traffic."

"Yeah, me too," said Edwardo. Then he stuck his left earbud back into his ear.

The traffic actually wasn't too bad for a Friday evening, and when they got to the parking lot of the sports arena, Anne Marie paid the parking attendant $10 so she could park in the arena's lot.

"Seems like a lot of money for parking," she said as she drove away from the attendant and started looking for a spot.

Edwardo wasn't listening to his iPod anymore. "Everything is pretty expensive when it comes to these kinds of concerts," he said. "Look at what we paid for the tickets."

"I know," Anne Marie said as she drove into a parking spot.

Anne Marie and Edwardo got out of the car, walked to the front entrance of the sports arena, and handed the man at the front door their tickets.

They had pretty good seats because Anne Marie said that it really wasn't worth going to a concert unless you had good seats. She had had bad seats one time and promised herself that she wasn't going to go to any more concerts unless she had saved up enough money to get a good seat. These tickets were good—not as good as you could get, but still pretty darn good.

"I wonder if the place will be packed," Edwardo said as they walked down the steps to their seats. "Do you know how many people the place will seat?" Edwardo asked.

"I heard it was 15,000," Anne Marie said.

"A crowd that size can make some noise," Edwardo said.

"Yeah, I know," said Anne Marie. Then she paused in front of row 3 and said, "We're right here. Seats 4 and 5."

The first thing that Edwardo did was look at the stage from where he was standing. "Nice seats," he said.

It was about 40 minutes before the concert was supposed to start. Roadies on the stage were setting things up, and recorded music played. Edwardo and Anne Marie sat in their seats for a while, looking around and talking.

"See anyone you know?" Edwardo asked.

"No," said Anne Marie, "although Mike said that he was coming. I'm not sure where he is sitting, though."

"Do you want to get something to eat?" Edwardo asked.

Anne Marie said that she did. And so the two of them got up from their seats and walked to one of the many concession stands nearby.

When a rock band takes the stage, there is the band, the fans, and the music. For the next 90 to 120 minutes, everyone's attention is almost always completely focused on the music and the concert experience. It is as if the rest of the world no longer exists.

But before that rock band takes the stage, and even before it decides it is going to tour, there are discussions. How many days should the band tour? What cities should the band visit? How many people should the band take on the road with them? Where should the band stay while on the road? How many people will be needed to set up the equipment? break down the equipment? load the equipment? and so on.

The particular rock band that Anne Marie and Edwardo were waiting to see this Friday night had been on the road nearly two months now. Eight months before they had first gone on tour, the members of the band had sat at the drummer's house and carried on the following conversation:

"I'm not sure how many cities we should play," Steven said.

"Jackson has proposed 75 cities," Kinumo said. Jackson was the band's manager.

"Yeah, I know," said Steven. "He told me the same thing. But maybe that's too many. How many cities we play depends on how much we get paid on average per city."

"More money per city, more cities?" Kinumo asked.

"Yeah, I think so," Steven said.

"I think it also depends on what we have to pay people to move the equipment and set up," Kenny interjected.

"We paid a lot last time for moving everything," Kinumo said. "You think we can do it for less this time?"

"Jackson thinks we can," Kenny answered.

"I'll tell you one thing that will make me more likely to visit more cities this time," Kinumo said.

"What?" Steven asked.

"The fact that I now have my primary residence in Florida. No state income taxes," Kinumo said.

"Yeah, I know. That is a nice bonus," Steven said. "I should move to a state that doesn't have a state income tax."

"So what do you think?" Kenny asked. "How many cities is it going to be?"

"I'm still not sure," Steven replied.

Find the Economics

Name the three most interesting economics ideas that you found "hidden" in this scene, and explain the clues that led you to discover them.

1. ______________________________

____

____

2. ______________________________

____

____

3. ______________________________

____

____

Name: ______________________________ Date: ______________

CHAPTER 6

Before you read the following scene, review Chapter 6 in the *Student Text*, focusing on the major concepts covered there. You may want to skim the chapter or read the Chapter Summary on page 168.

Now, with the economics concepts of Chapter 6 fresh in your mind, read "Holiday Shopping Snags" searching, like an economics detective, for the economics below the surface. The story contains a number of economics ideas, but they are hidden. It is your job to find them.

As you read, circle and underline words and phrases that you think are clues or connections to the economics embedded in the scene. Make notes in the margin. At the end of the scene, on the lines provided, write two or three sentences describing each of the three most interesting economics ideas that you found in the scene.

Holiday Shopping Snags

Notes

Background

On November 23, just a month before the wrap-up of the holiday shopping season, Econ2e, Inc. released the next edition of its hugely popular LarryFish gaming console in North America. Demand for the console made it nearly impossible to find and purchase the product for the holidays. According to a Fish-Watch article, "Since it launched, LarryFish 2e has been jumping off store shelves and is sold out at most major retailers." Econ2e issued the following statement: "The LarryFish team is working hard to meet consumer demand and we are delivering consoles to retailers as fast as possible this holiday season. We urge consumers to sign up on our website to receive email alerts from retailers and to look for the products at retailers in smaller communities where demand may be lower."

At about the same time a local business article reported a shortage of high-quality aquarium products. The article read, "The recent closing of New Waves Aquarium Arts has aquarium owners nervous about where they will find their favorite fishbowl and aquarium products. New Waves Aquarium Arts closed its Orange County, California, factory after producing an estimated 90 percent of the models and molds used to craft custom-made fishbowl and aquarium decorations." Retailers purchase the models and smooth them out before painters add custom colors and designs to each. In other words, the models are needed to produce the finished product.

It had been a holiday shopping season that Pam Rosenberg would not forget for a number of years. Pam had saved enough money to buy her two boys exactly what they wanted that year and was looking forward to when they would sit down to open their gifts. Pam's younger son wanted a LarryFish gaming system for Christmas. So, on November 23, the day it was to be released in stores, she got up bright and early and went to her local electronics store, ready to purchase the new gaming system.

"Where are the LarryFish consoles?" Pam asked the sales clerk in the store.

The clerk looked surprised. "Ah," he said, "they sold out early this morning. They were all gone by 6 a.m."

Pam's heart sank.

"But I thought you opened at nine," Pam said.

"We were open all last night," the clerk explained. "People were standing in line beginning at 9 p.m., waiting for the sale to begin at midnight."

"But that's crazy," Pam said.

"Yeah, I know," said the clerk. "Who would have thought it would turn out to be that popular?"

Pam, feeling somewhat at a loss as to what to do, left the store, got into her car, and just sat there for a few minutes. She wanted to get some of her gift shopping done today, so after a few minutes of thought, she started her car and headed over to the Pet Supply Shop, the largest retail aquarium shop in the area.

Pam knew which aquarium set her older son wanted for Christmas and knew that it would be within her budget. She pointed at the large aquarium set as a young sales clerk approached. But was shocked to see that the price was nearly double what she had been prepared to spend.

"Wasn't this set at a lower price a while back?" she asked the clerk.

"That's right," the saleswoman said. "It's because of New Waves Aquarium Arts."

"What's New Waves Aquarium Arts?" Pam asked.

"It's the company that makes the models for those sets. They closed down one of their factories. It's hard to get the models right now."

"But this set is twice as much as it used to be!"

"I know," said the clerk. "Almost all of the sets have gone up by that much."

Pam knew she couldn't justify spending that much on aquarium decorations, even if it was a gift. Pam left the shop, got into her car, and drove home. As she got out of the car, she had visions of herself as Scrooge. "I'm not sure what that was all about," she said to herself as she unlocked the front door of her house, then opened it and walked inside. She threw her jacket on the living room couch and sat down. So far, it hadn't been a very good day.

Find the Economics

Name the three most interesting economics ideas that you found "hidden" in this scene, and explain the clues that led you to discover them.

1. ____

____

____

2. ____

____

____

3. ____

____

____

Name: ______________________________ Date: ______________

CHAPTER 7

Before you read the following scene, review Chapter 7 in the *Student Text*, focusing on the major concepts covered there. You may want to skim the chapter or read the Chapter Summary on page 204.

Now, with the economics concepts of Chapter 7 fresh in your mind, read "The Group Project," searching, like an economics detective, for the economics below the surface. The story contains a number of economics ideas, but they are hidden. It is your job to find them.

As you read, circle and underline words and phrases that you think are clues or connections to the economics embedded in the scene. Make notes in the margin. At the end of the scene, on the lines provided, write two or three sentences describing each of the three most interesting economics ideas that you found in the scene.

The Group Project

Notes

The phone rang, and Federico walked across the kitchen to pick it up.

"Hello," he said.

"Have you seen Kyle today?" Ling Mei, a girl from his economics class, asked angrily.

Federico knew something was up. "I saw him for a few minutes after biology class. Why? What's going on?"

"He just sent his part of the project to me as an e-mail attachment. He's hardly done anything."

Federico felt an uneasiness in his stomach and he gulped hard. He knew what Kyle not doing his work meant for the group.

One month earlier, Federico, Kyle, and Ling Mei, along with Michael and Richelle, had been sitting in their economics class. Their teacher, Mrs. Yarnes, had assigned group projects. She placed Federico, Kyle, Ling Mei, Michael, and Richelle together in one group. Their group assignment was to write a 15-page paper and give a class presentation on the following topic: The Ins and Outs of Starting a Successful Franchise.

The students were supposed to get together in their free time (after school or on the weekends) and divide up the work. Each one was to do approximately one-fifth of the paper and presentation. Mrs. Yarnes told each group in class that the grade they received on their group paper and presentation would be the individual grade each student in the group received for the assignment. In other words, if the paper and presentation received a B+, then everyone in the group—all five members—would each receive a B+.

"Where do you think he is?" Ling Mei asked Federico. "I need to talk with him. I tried calling his house, but he's not there. I tried calling his cell, but no answer."

"I think he could be at the gym," Federico said. "He's been working out quite a bit recently."

"Yeah, working out instead of doing his work," Ling Mei said. "What's he working out for?"

"Baseball tryouts," Federico said. "They're in a few weeks. He wants to build up some strength in his arms and legs."

There was little doubt that Ling Mei wasn't really interested in Kyle's exercise regimen for baseball tryouts. She had more serious things on her mind. If she turned in Kyle's work the way it was, the overall grade for the project would be fairly low. Missing 20 percent of the project would surely hurt the group's grade.

"What do you think we should do?" Federico asked.

"Time is short. We've got to turn in the paper in a day, and we give the presentation in probably three days. Someone has to get Kyle's part of the project up to par. I'd like it to be Kyle, but as I said, I can't find him."

"Do you think he's really going to fix things?" Federico asked. He had his doubts.

"I would hope so," Ling Mei said. "He owes that much to the rest of us."

"Yeah, I know he owes it to us, but I'm not so sure he is going to do any more work. I think he would have done the work in the first place if he had wanted to."

"You're probably right about that," Ling Mei said. Then there was a pause on the phone.

"Ling Mei? You still there?"

"I was wondering how we are going to take care of this. I should probably call Michael and Richelle and tell them what has happened and see if they have any ideas on who is going to do Kyle's work."

"That might be a good idea. I don't mind doing some of it, but I don't want to do it all," Federico said.

"Same with me," Ling Mei said. "By the way," she added, "don't you think we should tell Mrs. Yarnes that Kyle didn't do his part of the project? I just hate the idea that we do our work, and his work too, and he gets the same grade as we do."

"I know what you mean," Federico said. "Why don't we talk it over with the others?"

"OK," Ling Mei replied. "I'll talk to you later. Bye."

"Bye," Federico said.

Meanwhile, Kyle was at the local gym. He had been going there after school for the past few weeks. He usually did some running on the treadmill and then turned his attention to weight lifting. Mainly, as Federico had said, he was interested in strengthening his arms and legs.

Notes

Kyle's membership to the gym cost $50 a month. He paid for his gym membership, and for a few other things, by working on the weekends at the Sports Shop near where he lived. As he moved from one machine to another in the gym, he thought about how he was really getting good use of his membership this month. Some months in the past, he had rarely visited the gym. But this month, he had visited 10 times. Not once while he was at the gym did the thought cross his mind that he hadn't done a good job on his part of the group project.

Find the Economics

Name the three most interesting economics ideas that you found "hidden" in this scene, and explain the clues that led you to discover them.

1. ______________________________

____

____

2. ______________________________

____

____

3. ______________________________

____

____

Name: ______________________________ Date: ______________

CHAPTER 8

Before you read the following scene, review Chapter 8 in the *Student Text*, focusing on the major concepts covered there. You may want to skim the chapter or read the Chapter Summary on page 242.

Now, with the economics concepts of Chapter 8 fresh in your mind, read "A Day in the Life of a Writer," searching, like an economics detective, for the economics below the surface. The story contains a number of economics ideas, but they are hidden. It is your job to find them.

As you read, circle and underline words and phrases that you think are clues or connections to the economics embedded in the scene. Make notes in the margin. At the end of the scene, on the lines provided, write two or three sentences describing each of the three most interesting economics ideas that you found in the scene.

A Day in the Life of a Writer

Notes

Aaron Spellman had had the same schedule now for at least the last 15 years. The routine settled him; it was predictable and that was what he liked. Aaron, 45 years old, lived with his wife, Margie, a physician, in what was probably Boston's most exclusive neighborhood, Beacon Hill.

Aaron and Margie could easily afford their house; she was a doctor, after all, and he had had seven books on the *New York Times* best-seller list in the last 10 years. Horror stories sold, especially when Aaron Spellman had written them.

With his last book, he had departed from his usual story and his usual style. *The Mountain* wasn't so much a horror story as it was a love story. His publisher had advised him against it, and so had his agent, but Aaron had wanted to try something different, and so he did. But the book hadn't been received well; it had gotten only half the sales of his other books, so Aaron knew that he had no choice but to return to what the people wanted from him, which was horror—good old-fashioned, check-what's-under-the-bed horror. As his agent had said to him before he had started on the love story, "You've spent years developing a brand name in horror, so why jeopardize all that hard work now? When your fans expect steak from you, and love the way you cook it, why serve them fish?"

Anyway, on this Tuesday, like all other days (he wrote every day of the week), Aaron got up at 8:30 a.m. and left his house by 9:00. Margie had already been up for two hours now. She was at the hospital tending to her patients.

Aaron walked the three blocks to the coffee shop he always went to, where he ordered his usual: a large regular coffee and a cheese

Danish. There were other coffee shops a little farther away, and he had thought about venturing out to patronize them someday, but so far he hadn't. This coffee shop fit into his schedule a lot better. It was close enough to his house to make things convenient, and he could get his coffee, eat his Danish, and read what he wanted to read in the newspaper in the time he had allotted for such things in the morning. He knew he wanted to be at his desk, working, by 10 a.m.

At 9:35 Aaron left the coffee shop and started walking back home. Once there, he went into his study, which was in the front of the house. He sat down at his large wooden desk, in front of a window overlooking the street, and turned on his computer. For the next 10 to 15 minutes he would check his stocks. He had built up quite a stock portfolio over the years. He checked to see how his stocks were doing, and then decided to sell 100 shares of two of the many stocks he owned. He checked their prices, put in an order to sell, and submitted the order with a click of his computer mouse.

It was now time to turn to his work. Aaron opened the folder titled "newest book" and then opened the file marked "Chapter 5." He read the last paragraph on the page. He worked until three in the afternoon. For him, five hours a day was about all the productive work—good writing—he could do. Any more time spent at work would be useless.

Find the Economics

Name the three most interesting economics ideas that you found "hidden" in this scene, and explain the clues that led you to discover them.

1. ____

____

____

2. ____

____

____

3. ____

____

____

Name: ______________________ Date: ____________

CHAPTER 9

Before you read the following scene, review Chapter 9 in the *Student Text*, focusing on the major concepts covered there. You may want to skim the chapter or read the Chapter Summary on page 270.

Now, with the economics concepts of Chapter 9 fresh in your mind, read "Burbank, California," searching, like an economics detective, for the economics below the surface. The story contains a number of economics ideas, but they are hidden. It is your job to find them.

As you read, circle and underline words and phrases that you think are clues or connections to the economics embedded in the scene. Make notes in the margin. At the end of the scene, on the lines provided, write two or three sentences describing each of the three most interesting economics ideas that you found in the scene.

Burbank, California

Notes

The sun shines brightly and cars move slowly. Smog lies in front of the mountains in the distance. Radios in the cars are tuned to a wide variety of stations; people talk on their cell phones as they drive along. This is LA—Los Angeles—at 8:04 a.m. on Wednesday, and the scene is repeated five times a week, every week of the year.

The people in these cars are headed to various businesses in Burbank. Many of them work in the entertainment business, since Burbank is the home of several TV studios, including ABC, Nickelodeon, Warner Brothers, and Disney. Three miles away from his exit, Jonathan Wilson, 28, drives along in his three-year-old Toyota Corolla. Jonathan works as an animation artist at Disney. Disney's last animated film did unusually well, and for him that spells job security and maybe a bonus.

Stephanie Hendrix, 19 years old, is a college student at nearby UCLA and works as a tour guide at Nickelodeon's Studios. She shows visitors the studio where TV shows are filmed.

Hoa Nguyen is in her BMW heading toward the Warner Brothers studio. She is a cameraperson on a show that which is filmed on a back lot at the studio. Friends of hers, who know where she works, often comment to her how nice Ridgeville looks on TV. Ridgeville is the make-believe small town in Connecticut where the main characters on the show live.

"You'd never think it was a back lot in Burbank," one friend says.

"That's the magic of television," Hoa says.

Notes

The union to which Hoa belongs is thinking of calling a strike. It seems that camera operators' wages haven't substantially risen in some time, and although there was a small raise last year, it didn't do that much for the workers because prices rose at a faster rate than their wages.

Just taking the Burbank exit is Tim Wagoner, who plays Dr. Dirk Stevens on one of ABC's hottest shows. He hasn't shaved today because the studio told him not to. Today's scene is an early morning scene in his new condo, overlooking the ocean. Dr. Dirk Stevens is new in town—in the make-believe town on TV, that is—and Tim has already gotten his picture in most of the entertainment magazines.

Yesterday, after work, he was at his home in Encino, hanging out by his pool with a friend. "How's work going?" his friend asked.

"Great," Tim said. "I like it so much I'd do the job for half the pay." Then he leaned over and whispered, "But don't tell the studio that."

Find the Economics

Name the three most interesting economics ideas that you found "hidden" in this scene, and explain the clues that led you to discover them.

1. ______________________________

____

____

2. ______________________________

____

____

3. ______________________________

____

____

Name: ______________________ Date: ______________

CHAPTER 10

Before you read the following scene, review Chapter 10 in the *Student Text*, focusing on the major concepts covered there. You may want to skim the chapter or read the Chapter Summary on page 312.

Now, with the economics concepts of Chapter 10 fresh in your mind, read "Phillip Baldwin," searching, like an economics detective, for the economics below the surface. The story contains a number of economics ideas, but they are hidden. It is your job to find them.

As you read, circle and underline words and phrases that you think are clues or connections to the economics embedded in the scene. Make notes in the margin. At the end of the scene, on the lines provided, write two or three sentences describing each of the three most interesting economics ideas that you found in the scene.

Phillip Baldwin

Notes

My perception of time is not always the same. For example, sometimes it seems that time moves fast. I'm 58 now, and when I look back on my life when I was, say, 17, it doesn't seem that long ago. For instance, I remember when I was 17, in 1973, I attended the concert Led Zeppelin gave at Madison Square Garden in New York City. There on the stage was what is generally considered to be one of the greatest bands of all time. There was John Bonham on drums, John Paul Jones on keyboard and guitar, Jimmy Page on guitar, and Robert Plant on vocals.

Anyway, that was back then, as I said, but it still seems as if it were only last year.

Then there are things that I did only last month that seem like they happened years ago. I went on a business trip last month to Cleveland. I left LaGuardia at around 10 o'clock in the morning, got to Cleveland in no time at all, spent three days there, had dinner with some old friends, and returned to New York. Like I said, it was only last month, but it seems like a long time ago.

Odd that Zeppelin seems like only a year ago and the trip to Cleveland seems like years ago. I wonder what is going on here.

I should introduce myself. My name is Phillip Baldwin. I'm 58 years old, as I mentioned earlier, and I work at the lower end of Manhattan. I've worked there for 25 years. I buy and sell government securities for my clients. Most of my clients are fairly large institutions.

I live on the Upper East Side of Manhattan on 78th Street. I've lived in the same location for 10 years. I've pretty much done the same thing for the last 10 years too. I get up each morning at 7 a.m., shave and shower, get dressed and eat breakfast (usually just some cereal and orange juice), and then take the elevator down to the lobby, where, for the last eight of the past 10 years, the same doorman has held the door open for me as I walk out of the building. We're on a first-name basis.

"Good morning, Phil," he says to me.

"Good morning, Bill," I say to him.

Then he wishes me a good day and I wish him the same. Every now and then I stop and we chat about this or that—usually sports. In the summer we often talk about the Mets. This time of year, we talk about the Knicks.

I walk one block to the subway station, take it to the lower end of Manhattan, get out, walk up the stairs, and then get a coffee at a small stand at the top of the stairs. The same guy has been working the coffee stand for the past five years.

I then walk a block to my building. I take the elevator up to the 31st floor, get out, walk a few feet to my office, and then get to work.

I like my job, and I probably wouldn't change it for another, but there are days that I feel a little burned out, if you know what I mean. That probably happens to everybody. You do something long enough and it becomes routine; it loses a little of its initial excitement.

As I've gotten older, I've really come to enjoy the weekends more. I have a family—a wife, two sons, and one daughter. The daughter is 18 years old and is going off to college next year. The boys are older: one is 20 and the other is 22. They're both in college. One goes to the University of Pennsylvania in Philadelphia and the other goes to NYU, right here in Manhattan. I wanted him to go elsewhere. I told him that he should get out of the city for college, but he wanted to stay here. He kept saying that NYU is an exciting place and it has everything that he wants to study right there and why should he go anywhere else.

He hasn't regretted his decision so far, and I'm glad of that.

My wife took some time off from her job for a while when we first had kids, but she went back to work when our daughter was 12 years old. She works at the Marriott Marquis Hotel, right down in Times Square. She works behind the front desk, checking people in and out of the hotel. She likes the job a lot; she says she gets to meet all kinds of people. On any given day, there are people from all over the country and the world checking into that hotel.

Every now and then I meet her at the hotel after work and we go out to dinner. Both of us like to eat in restaurants, and there is probably no better place to find a variety of cuisine at great restaurants than in New York.

Anyway, I guess that's all I have to say for now. I had better get to work. Have a nice day, won't you?

Find the Economics

Name the three most interesting economics ideas that you found "hidden" in this scene, and explain the clues that led you to discover them.

1. ____

____

____

2. ____

____

____

3. ____

____

____

Name: ______________________________ Date: ______________

CHAPTER 11

Before you read the following scene, review Chapter 11 in the *Student Text*, focusing on the major concepts covered there. You may want to skim the chapter or read the Chapter Summary on page 342.

Now, with the economics concepts of Chapter 11 fresh in your mind, read "Saturday at the Mall," searching, like an economics detective, for the economics below the surface. The story contains a number of economics ideas, but they are hidden. It is your job to find them.

As you read, circle and underline words and phrases that you think are clues or connections to the economics embedded in the scene. Make notes in the margin. At the end of the scene, on the lines provided, write two or three sentences describing each of the three most interesting economics ideas that you found in the scene.

Saturday at the Mall

Notes

It is located in Bloomington, Minnesota, only five minutes from the Minneapolis-St. Paul International Airport. It has over 520 stores, hosts more than 400 events each year, and has 11,000 permanent employees. It is big enough to hold 32 Boeing 747s or seven Yankee stadiums. It is the Mall of America, and this Saturday morning, Amanda and Jaime are shopping there. As they walk toward a popular clothing store, they talk.

"How did you do on that biology test?" Amanda asks.

"I think I did OK," Jaime replies, "except for maybe that last essay question. I thought that one was really hard."

"Yeah, me too," Amanda says.

Just then Jaime's cell phone rings. Amanda notices that Jaime has a new cell phone.

"Hello," Jaime says. She listens while the caller talks. After about 30 seconds she turns off the phone. "It was my mom," she tells Amanda. "She's decided to buy that sweater for my aunt. It's her birthday next week. She wants me to buy it and she will pay me back."

"New cell phone?" Amanda asks.

"Yeah, I just got it a few days ago. It's a Samsung."

At the store the girls go their own ways. Amanda looks at jeans while Jaime looks at the tops. Jaime holds up a top to her while she looks in the mirror. She likes it; still, Jaime looks at more tops. You never know when you'll find one that looks better, she thinks.

Amanda tries on a pair of jeans. Not that it matters to her, but she notices that they were made in China. They look good on her and so she decides to buy them. She walks over to Jaime and says, "How's it going? Find what you like?"

"I think so," Jaime says slowly and deliberately, obviously still thinking about what would be best for her to buy.

"I'll be over here," Amanda says to Jaime, as she points.

"I'll just be a few more minutes," Jaime says.

Then Amanda says "Do you want to see a movie? Mrs. Gonzalez said we should see that new science fiction flick." Mrs. Gonzalez is one of the English teachers at the high school that Jaime and Amanda attend.

"Sure, I want to see it," Jaime says.

After they shop for another hour, they walk by the movie theater to see when the next showing will start: 1:30 p.m. They decide to eat lunch at Johnny Rockets.

"I shouldn't be eating this hamburger and shake," Amanda says, smiling.

I'm not going to make the varsity soccer team if I do this too often."

"You're great at soccer," Jaime says to Amanda. "You don't have anything to worry about."

"Yeah? Thanks!" says Amanda. Then she changes the subject. "I've heard that the movie is really popular. I hope the theater isn't too crowded."

"Yeah, I know," Jaime says. "I hate it when people are all around me. I like to have an empty seat between me and the next person so I can stretch out."

"Me too," Amanda says. Then she notices two guys from school, Nicky and Michael, coming into the restaurant. "There are Nicky and Michael," she says to Jaime. Jaime turns to look.

"You sort of like Nicky, don't you?" she asks Amanda.

"Yeah, I think he's OK," Amanda says.

Jaime looks at her watch. "Well, are you about ready to head on over to the movie?" Jaime asks.

"Yeah, let's go," she replies, but Jaime can tell that all of a sudden Amanda is less interested in watching the movie.

Find the Economics

Name the three most interesting economics ideas that you found "hidden" in this scene, and explain the clues that led you to discover them.

1. ____________________

____

____

2. ____________________

____

____

3. ____________________

____

____

Name: ______________________ Date: ______________

CHAPTER 12

Before you read the following scene, review Chapter 12 in the *Student Text*, focusing on the major concepts covered there. You may want to skim the chapter or read the Chapter Summary on page 374.

Now, with the economics concepts of Chapter 12 fresh in your mind, read "Caroline and Her Grandparents," searching, like an economics detective, for the economics below the surface. The story contains a number of economics ideas, but they are hidden. It is your job to find them.

As you read, circle and underline words and phrases that you think are clues or connections to the economics embedded in the scene. Make notes in the margin. At the end of the scene, on the lines provided, write two or three sentences describing each of the three most interesting economics ideas that you found in the scene.

Caroline and Her Grandparents

Notes

Caroline lived with her grandparents and had just started her senior year at Patrick Henry High School. Soon, she would start applying to colleges. She wanted to go somewhere out of state, but she knew an in-state college would be cheaper. She wanted to major in math. Her grandfather was proud that she did. He would say, "You have to be smart to major in math, and I know you are."

Caroline's grandparents were really nice people. Her grandfather, Bill, had worked for the power company in town for 40 years; he retired two years ago at the age of 65. Her grandmother had been a middle-school mathematics teacher. Caroline's grandfather had said that Caroline had gotten her math ability from her grandmother. It was last year that Caroline's grandmother, Mary, retired from teaching. Occasionally, Mary says that she misses the students.

Caroline generally liked living with her grandparents, except that, now and then, they were a little too old-fashioned for her liking. They sometimes complained about the clothes she wanted to wear. They thought some items weren't appropriate for school.

"Everybody wears this," Caroline would say.

It was usually her grandfather who said that he didn't think something was appropriate, but in the end, both he and Mary gave in begrudgingly.

"She's 17," Caroline's grandmother would say, "and I guess she is old enough to decide what she wants to wear. Maybe we are being a little old-fashioned."

"Well, old-fashioned might be better than new-fashioned," Bill would say, "at least when it comes to some things."

Mary couldn't really argue with that because deep down, she believed the same thing.

Notes

Bill, Mary, and Caroline lived in a 30-year-old house in a neighborhood about two miles from the high school. In recent years, the price of their house had risen. It was a comfortable house, with four bedrooms and a big family room. Last year, Bill and Mary bought a large LCD HDTV and put it in the big family room. "We watch a lot of television now that we're retired," Caroline's grandfather often said.

Right now, the two of them were watching the events in Fort Lauderdale. Three days ago a hurricane had slammed into the city, and the TV news was covering the story almost every minute of the day.

"I just can't believe all the damage that the hurricane did to that city," Mary said.

"I know," said Bill. "It is a mess down there. And it is so sad for so many people. It might be years before some people put their lives back together again."

"Doesn't it seem like more and more natural disasters are occurring?" Bill said, as he continued to watch the events in Fort Lauderdale unfold on TV.

"Are you referring to the tsunami a while back?" Mary asked.

"Yes," said Bill. "Where was that again? Wasn't it in Indonesia or near there? The people seemed so poor; they didn't need anything like a tsunami hitting them."

"No one needs a tsunami," Mary said.

"Oh, you know what I mean," Bill said.

"I guess you're right, because there have been a lot of hurricanes this season," said Mary.

"I don't see why the government doesn't just print more money and give it to the people in Fort Lauderdale who have lost their houses," Bill said.

"Wouldn't that cause inflation?" Mary asked.

"Well, maybe a little," Bill said. "But I'm sure it is not going to boost the inflation rate too high. So what if it raises prices by one-half of 1 percent?"

"Are you sure that is what it would be?" Mary asked.

"To tell you the truth, I'm not sure what it would be," Bill said. "But something has to be done to help the people who have been hurt so badly."

"I agree," said Mary.

Just then Caroline came into the room. "I'm going out for a little bit," she said.

"Be careful," her grandmother said.

"Yeah, don't drive too fast," her grandfather said.

"I won't," Caroline said. And with those words she left.

Find the Economics

Name the three most interesting economics ideas that you found "hidden" in this scene, and explain the clues that led you to discover them.

1. ______________________________

____

____

2. ______________________________

____

____

3. ______________________________

____

____

Name: _______________ Date: _______________

CHAPTER 13

Before you read the following scene, review Chapter 13 in the *Student Text*, focusing on the major concepts covered there. You may want to skim the chapter or read the Chapter Summary on page 402.

Now, with the economics concepts of Chapter 13 fresh in your mind, read "On the Plane," searching, like an economics detective, for the economics below the surface. The story contains a number of economics ideas, but they are hidden. It is your job to find them.

As you read, circle and underline words and phrases that you think are clues or connections to the economics embedded in the scene. Make notes in the margin. At the end of the scene, on the lines provided, write two or three sentences describing each of the three most interesting economics ideas that you found in the scene.

On the Plane

Notes

"Do you live in Chicago?" the man in the next seat asked. The plane was full and the pilot had asked everyone to be seated. The plane, bound for Chicago, was fifth in line to take off.

"Yes, I do," the other man replied. "You too?"

"Yeah," his seat neighbor said. "I've lived there all my life. What do you do?"

This conversation was moving along too fast for the man with the chatty seat neighbor. If the truth be known, he had bought a book in the airport bookstore a few hours ago, and already he was absorbed in it. He wanted to get back to it. He didn't want to talk; he just wanted to read. Least of all, he didn't really want to tell the man what he did for a living. That always brought on more questions. The question caught him off guard this time, and before he knew it he had answered it.

"I'm an economist," he said.

"I took an economics course in college," his neighbor said. "I didn't do too well in it, though. I thought the material was too abstract. It didn't really have to do with real life—all the diagrams and curves and everything."

The economist just smiled. He was willing to accept that; he would have accepted anything. All he wanted to do was read his book. Maybe at another time he would have wanted to engage the man in conversation. Sometimes, plane conversations could be enjoyable. But not now.

"You work for a company?" the economist's neighbor asked.

"Yes," the economist said. "I work for an economics consulting firm. Our clients want to know how macroeconomic events will affect their businesses. We help them to figure out those kinds of things."

"That sounds kind of interesting," the second man said.

The plane took off, and then began rising higher and higher into the air.

"It can be," the economist said.

"So, what do you think of what Congress is doing right now?" his neighbor asked. "I think those tax cuts are simply going to make the budget deficit worse. Do you?"

"That's not always guaranteed," the economist said. "We've had tax cuts before that actually raised tax revenue."

"I didn't know that," his neighbor said. "It just seemed to reason that if you cut someone's taxes, the government is naturally going to take in less money. It's sort of like cutting the price of a car. The car dealership that does that is going to take in less money on that car."

"On *that* car," the economist said. "But the car dealership might just end up selling more cars."

"I see what you mean," his neighbor said. "I guess that could be true."

Resigning himself to the fact that he would not be reading his book soon, the economist asked, "What do you do?" He wanted to get the conversation off economics.

"Oh, me? I appraise commercial buildings that companies want to sell. I have to travel a lot in my job."

"Do you mind traveling?"

"No, I kind of like it. I like to get out of the office and see the country. I like people, too," he said. "You learn things from people—just like I learned something from you just now."

"Any place in particular you really like?" the economist asked the man.

"Oh, well, not really," his neighbor answered. Then he thought about it for a minute and said, "I guess if you pushed me to the wall, I'd say that Seattle and Austin are two cities I enjoy visiting."

"Yeah, I know what you mean. They are nice cities."

"I took my oldest daughter with me the last time I went to Austin. It was the first time she had ever visited. Now she wants to apply to UT Austin. She's a senior in high school."

"It's a great college."

"Yeah, I know. I just wish she would go to a college a little closer to home, like my son did. That way I could see her a little more."

"I know that feeling," the economist said. He was enjoying the conversation more than he thought he would.

Two hours later they landed in Chicago. The two travelers had chatted the entire trip.

"It was good talking with you," they both said at the same time.

And then they went their separate ways.

Find the Economics

Name the three most interesting economics ideas that you found "hidden" in this scene, and explain the clues that led you to discover them.

1. ____

____

____

2. ____

____

____

3. ____

____

____

Name: ______________________________ Date: ______________

CHAPTER 14

Before you read the following scene, review Chapter 14 in the *Student Text*, focusing on the major concepts covered there. You may want to skim the chapter or read the Chapter Summary on page 426.

Now, with the economics concepts of Chapter 14 fresh in your mind, read "Sitting Around the Dinner Table," searching, like an economics detective, for the economics below the surface. The story contains a number of economics ideas, but they are hidden. It is your job to find them.

As you read, circle and underline words and phrases that you think are clues or connections to the economics embedded in the scene. Make notes in the margin. At the end of the scene, on the lines provided, write two or three sentences describing each of the three most interesting economics ideas that you found in the scene.

Sitting Around the Dinner Table

Notes

They had met years ago in Germany. Jack had been with the U.S. Army, stationed in Germany. Anna was German and had just graduated from high school. They met on a road one Saturday. She had rear-ended the car he was driving.

They both got out of their cars to see what damage had been done: not much. They got to talking and it was not hard to see that each liked the other. He asked her out on a date. She accepted. And the rest, as they say, is history.

Anna and Jack got married, and when his term in Germany was over, they made their home in Iowa, where Jack had grown up. It was there, in Des Moines, to be exact, where their two children were born.

Now they lived in Wyoming. He was a salesman for a software company and she was a physician's assistant. They both liked their jobs immensely. Rarely did either of them say they were burned out or tired of doing the same thing.

One of the things they liked doing most, which they had started when the kids were young, was sitting down at the dinner table and talking about what had happened during the day.

The kids knew the first words that would be spoken as they all sat down to eat. Either their dad or mom would say, "So, what happened today?"

Some days the kids wanted to say what was on their minds, especially if something out-of-the-ordinary had happened. Some days there really wasn't that much to say. It was always easy to tell who at the table had had the most exciting day, because that person always spoke up first.

"I got on the volleyball team at school," Nick had said two weeks ago.

"I got an A on that biology test I was worried about," Susana had said one week ago.

Tonight, no one seemed to want to start.

"I guess I'll go first," Anna said, as she looked around at everyone else. "Doesn't look like we have any big news tonight."

She continued, "I had this guy in the office today who thought surely he was deathly sick. I kept telling him that his symptoms were those of a bad cold, and that the stomachache was nothing to worry about. But he was sure that his stomach pains were the early signs of stomach cancer."

"I sort of feel sorry for people like that," Susana said. "They make life worse than it already is."

"You think life is bad?" Jack asked.

"I didn't mean it that way," Susana said. "I just mean that when you're a hypochondriac, like this guy no doubt is, you make life bad for yourself. It doesn't have to be that way; that's all I meant."

Nick said, "Dad knew what you meant. He's just trying to get the conversation started."

Susana looked at Nick and knew that he was right. She had seen that ploy before, and she wondered why she continued to fall for it.

"What did you do at work today, Dad?" Susana asked.

"Actually," he said, "I made a fairly big sale to a company in Minnesota. I've known this guy for years and I thought he was going to make a big purchase and it turns out that he did."

"Bonus time," Nick said.

"Well, maybe," his dad said.

"I ran into Kathy today on the way home from work," Anna said. "She said Joe was a little worried about his job with the company. Anything going on there?"

"There may be some cutbacks in Joe's division," Jack said. "I heard a little about that."

"Will that affect you?" Anna asked.

"Luckily for me, not at all," Jack said. "Where'd you run into Kathy?"

"I stopped by the art shop to buy some picture frames on my way home and I saw her there. She was buying some canvases."

"She really does like to paint, doesn't she?" Susana said.

"Oh, yeah," said her mother. "She's so good too. I'm thinking of buying a painting she did of an old farmhouse in a valley. It is really nice."

"What about you?" Jack said to Susana. "Anything special happen today?"

"No, not really," she said. "Pretty much the same old stuff. I've got a lot of homework tonight, though. This big English Lit paper is due in two days."

"You want me to look it over?" her dad asked.

"Last time you did that, I got a B– on the paper. You'd better let me take care of the papers, Dad."

"Whatever you say," her dad said.

Find the Economics

Name the three most interesting economics ideas that you found "hidden" in this scene, and explain the clues that led you to discover them.

1. ____

____

____

2. ____

____

____

3. ____

____

____

Name: ______________________________ Date: ____________

CHAPTER 15

Before you read the following scene, review Chapter 15 in the *Student Text*, focusing on the major concepts covered there. You may want to skim the chapter or read the Chapter Summary on page 466.

Now, with the economics concepts of Chapter 15 fresh in your mind, read "The Trip to London," searching, like an economics detective, for the economics below the surface. The story contains a number of economics ideas, but they are hidden. It is your job to find them.

As you read, circle and underline words and phrases that you think are clues or connections to the economics embedded in the scene. Make notes in the margin. At the end of the scene, on the lines provided, write two or three sentences describing each of the three most interesting economics ideas that you found in the scene.

The Trip to London

Notes

Megan had finally saved up enough money to take the trip with her friends; they would travel tomorrow. The plane would leave St. Louis at 7:30 a.m. and arrive in New York two and one-half hours later. The layover in New York was four hours. Then they'd get to do what they had planned for so long: take the trip to London. They would stay in London four days, and then go to Paris, where they planned to stay for another four days, and then they'd head to Spain.

Megan had wanted to take the trip after high school, but she hadn't saved up enough money. Now, three years later, she and her friends, Melanie and Marisabel—they called themselves the three M's—were ready to go.

She still had to pack and take care of some business at the office, so time was short, but that was usually when problems happened. Her laptop went on the blink. She wanted to take it with her on the trip. That way she could send some pictures back home and check her office e-mail too, although she wasn't sure how often she wanted to check her office e-mail.

Megan had purchased the laptop two years ago. Everything had been OK up until now. She found the company's service number and called it. Over the phone, she gave her name and express code number, and then a technician came on the line. He was sitting in a cubicle in a large room in India.

"Hello, my name is Jayant," he said. "Can I have your phone number, please?"

Megan gave him the number.

"May I also have your service tag number?" he asked.

Megan gave him the service tag number.

"OK, then, may I help you?" Jayant said.

Megan went through what was wrong with her computer. Jayant looked into some manuals, asked her to do this and that, and in a matter of minutes he had diagnosed and fixed the trouble. Megan was relieved to find out that she didn't have a big problem. She didn't have time to deal with a big problem.

Megan, Melanie, and Marisabel's flight left New York a little later than scheduled. It seemed that there was a "small mechanical problem with the plane," as the pilot said—is any problem a small problem on an airplane?—that the mechanics had to investigate. They fixed it in about 30 minutes, said the plane was ready to go, and off it went.

When Megan, Melanie, and Marisabel arrived at Heathrow Airport in London, it was early morning. They had traveled most of the night and were tired but excited. The first thing they did was collect their luggage at the baggage claim, and then they proceeded through Customs. They all had their passports stamped and off they went. Marisabel said that it would be a lot cheaper if they took the Underground (subway) into London from Heathrow, but no one was sure where to get on the Underground and what train changes, if any, they would have to make.

"Why don't we take a taxi this time?" Melanie asked.

"It'll be at least three times more expensive," Marisabel said. "Which reminds me," she added, "we have to get our money changed into pounds."

"We should do that right away," Megan said.

And so they did. At the current exchange rate between the British pound and the U.S. dollar, things were not looking good for Americans. The dollar was worth only a little more than half of the pound.

While Megan and Melanie were getting their dollars changed for pounds, Marisabel managed to get a map of the Underground. As Megan and Melanie approached Marisabel, she said, "I don't think getting to our hotel is going to be hard at all. From this map, it looks like we only have to make one change."

"We'll follow you, then," Megan said.

Once on the Underground, Megan said she was glad they had taken the subway instead of a taxi. "You see more people down here," she said.

"And you save a lot of money too," Marisabel reminded her.

In about 30 minutes, they reached the Underground station nearest to their hotel. They got off the train, walked up two flights of steps, and walked out of the rather large station and into the London air. Red double-decker buses, as well as numerous black taxis, waited for customers in front of the station.

"Should we take a taxi to the hotel?" Melanie asked. "It looks like it might be a little too far to walk."

Everyone agreed. A taxi it was.

They got into the big black taxi, sat back, and enjoyed the moment. "Are you three from the States?" the cabbie asked them.

"Yes, we are," Marisabel replied.

"Welcome to London," he said. "I'm sure you're going to enjoy yourselves here. It's a grand city."

Marisabel, Melanie, and Megan smiled. "We can't wait," Megan said.

Find the Economics

Name the three most interesting economics ideas that you found "hidden" in this scene, and explain the clues that led you to discover them.

1. ______________________________

____

____

2. ______________________________

____

____

3. ______________________________

____

____

Name: ______________________________ Date: ______________

CHAPTER 16

Before you read the following scene, review Chapter 16 in the *Student Text*, focusing on the major concepts covered there. You may want to skim the chapter or read the Chapter Summary on page 498.

Now, with the economics concepts of Chapter 16 fresh in your mind, read "Tralfamadorians," searching, like an economics detective, for the economics below the surface. The story contains a number of economics ideas, but they are hidden. It is your job to find them.

As you read, circle and underline words and phrases that you think are clues or connections to the economics embedded in the scene. Make notes in the margin. At the end of the scene, on the lines provided, write two or three sentences describing each of the three most interesting economics ideas that you found in the scene.

Tralfamadorians

Notes

I was reading *Slaughterhouse-Five* the other day. It was written by Kurt Vonnegut, and it's about this guy, Billy Pilgrim, who was in World War II. Billy says that on the night of his daughter's wedding, he was kidnapped and taken to the planet Tralfamadore. Billy says that the creatures on Tralfamadore were friendly and that they could see in four dimensions. Needless to say, human beings on the planet Earth can't see in four dimensions.

There is all this other stuff about how Tralfamadorians experience time, but that is not as relevant to what I want to say. I want to talk about dimensions that we are unaware of. Actually, to be a little more precise, I want to talk about things that go on every day in this country, and in this world, that we are unaware of.

Let me give you an example of what I mean. As I write this, I am sitting in a room typing out words on my computer keyboard. Now, to tell you the truth, I don't think about my computer very much. I just sit down at it, and either go online or start writing in my word processing program. If I wanted to look closer at the computer, though, I could learn more about it and about the world in which I live.

For example, if I take the computer apart, I could learn about its different parts. I might not know about all the parts, but I would be able to set them down on my desk and say, here is one part, here is another part, and here is a third part. I bet some of those parts were made by companies in other countries.

If I look a little closer—but this time I have to look with my mind instead of my eyes—I bet I could identify the companies that manufactured various parts.

But then that leads me to ask, How did the computer company get money to build the factories that manufactured my computer? I bet the company had to issue either stock or bonds to get the money.

And if I look even closer, I would have to realize that someone had to buy those shares of stock and those bonds. I would bet you that there is an investment manager who bought some shares of stock in the company that made my computer. I bet he bought those shares of stock to add to a portfolio of stocks that will ultimately be used to pay off someone's retirement benefits. In other words, if I look closely enough,
I can see in my mind the retired person who will get a retirement check based on the stocks an investment manager bought in the company that made my computer.

See how many people are "in" my computer?

Now I know I am not seeing in the fourth dimension in the same way that Tralfamadorians see in a fourth dimension, but if you look at something like a computer closely enough, you can see a lot more than a monitor, a keyboard, and a mouse.

Let me give you another example. This morning I made myself two pieces of toast. I put some peanut butter and grape jelly on the toast and ate it with a small glass of milk.

If you look closely enough, you can see a lot in a piece of bread that you put in a toaster. There is the bread, of course. But the bread is made from wheat. The wheat is grown by a farmer on a farm.

Now maybe that farmer was worried about the price at which she would sell her wheat. Maybe she was worried about the price of wheat six months before she even harvested her wheat. Maybe she was so worried that she entered into a futures contract specifying that she would sell her wheat at a certain price in six months.

In other words, as that piece of bread is popping out of the toaster, there could be a long story to tell: a story that runs from the grocery store, to the wholesaler, to the baker, to the farmer, to a futures contract.

How many people are popping up with that piece of toast? How many people are sitting down to breakfast with me as I put peanut butter and jelly on my toast?

Here's what I think. I think Billy Pilgrim, the main character in *Slaughterhouse-Five*, was onto something when he said that the Tralfamadorians could see in a fourth dimension. I think if we learn to focus on things hard enough, maybe we can see in more "dimensions" than we think we can.

A lamp is not just a lamp. It is a company that makes the lamp, workers in the factory where the lamp is made, shares of stock that the company issues to get the money to build the factory, and so on.

Lamps don't just appear out of thin air. By the time they reach your desk or end table, they have traveled a long way, and they have a story to tell, if only we know how to read that story.

Find the Economics

Name the three most interesting economics ideas that you found "hidden" in this scene, and explain the clues that led you to discover them.

1. ______________________________

____

____

2. ______________________________

____

____

3. ______________________________

____

____